A BOOK OF THINGS

By

Freddie McKeown

© THE MEDICI SOCIETY LTD · LONDON · 1993. Printed in England. ISBN 0 85503 098 4

TASTY THINGS

Corn on the cob,
bananas and bread,
little sweets too ~
yellow and red!
Fresh fruit and vegetables
ripe for the picking,
sausages on sticks
and swiss-rolls for licking!

*

Now last but not least,
to finish the feast,
out of the pan jumps ...
THE GINGER~BREAD MAN!

NOISY THINGS

An organ , a drum
or acoustic guitar .
A spotty dog barking,
the horn of a car !
A bell or a hammer,
a bird in full song .
A telephone ringing ,
a bang on a gong !

*

A cat caterwauling,
a new shoe that creaks,
and now something quiet...
A TEDDY WHO SQUEAKS !

KITCHEN THINGS

A fridge and a cooker,
a washing machine,
a squeezy sponge mop —
to wash the floors clean!
Utensils, a toast rack,
some pots and some pans,
a spice rack with spices
or various jams.

*

Without all these treasures
it is not complete,
and there to stand guard...
AN EGG CUP WITH FEET!

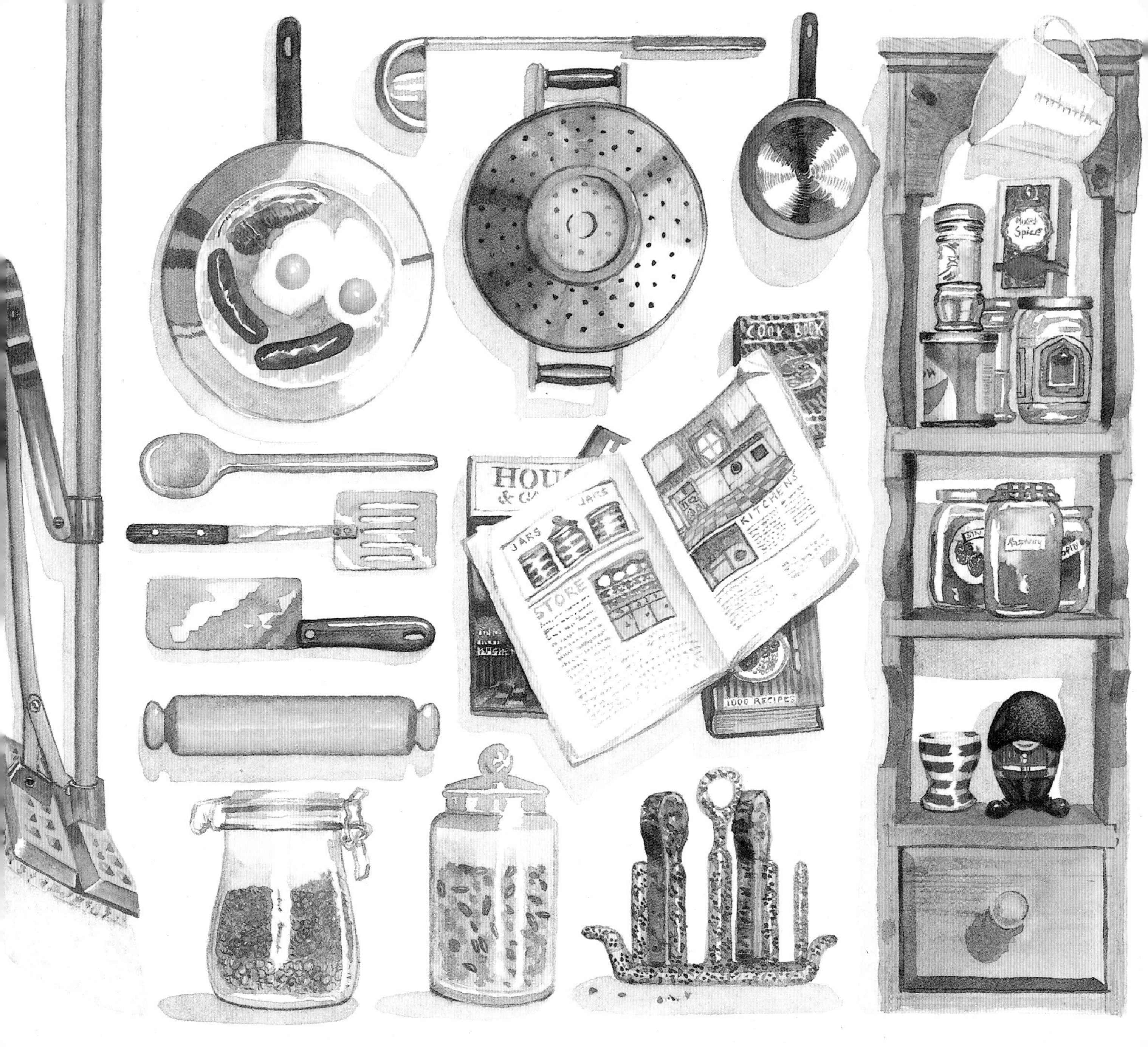
COOK BOOK
Mixed Spice
HOUS
JARS
JARS
STORE
KITCHENS
Raspberry
1000 RECIPES

SPIKEY THINGS

A fircone, a toothbrush
the ends of a brolly,
a comb or a hairbrush,
a sprig of green holly!
A juicy pineapple,
a knight's club for hitting,
a thistle, a teazle,
a needle for knitting.

★

Things that are spikey—
quite big and quite small,
and OUCH! There's a hedgehog
.... ROLLED UP LIKE A BALL!

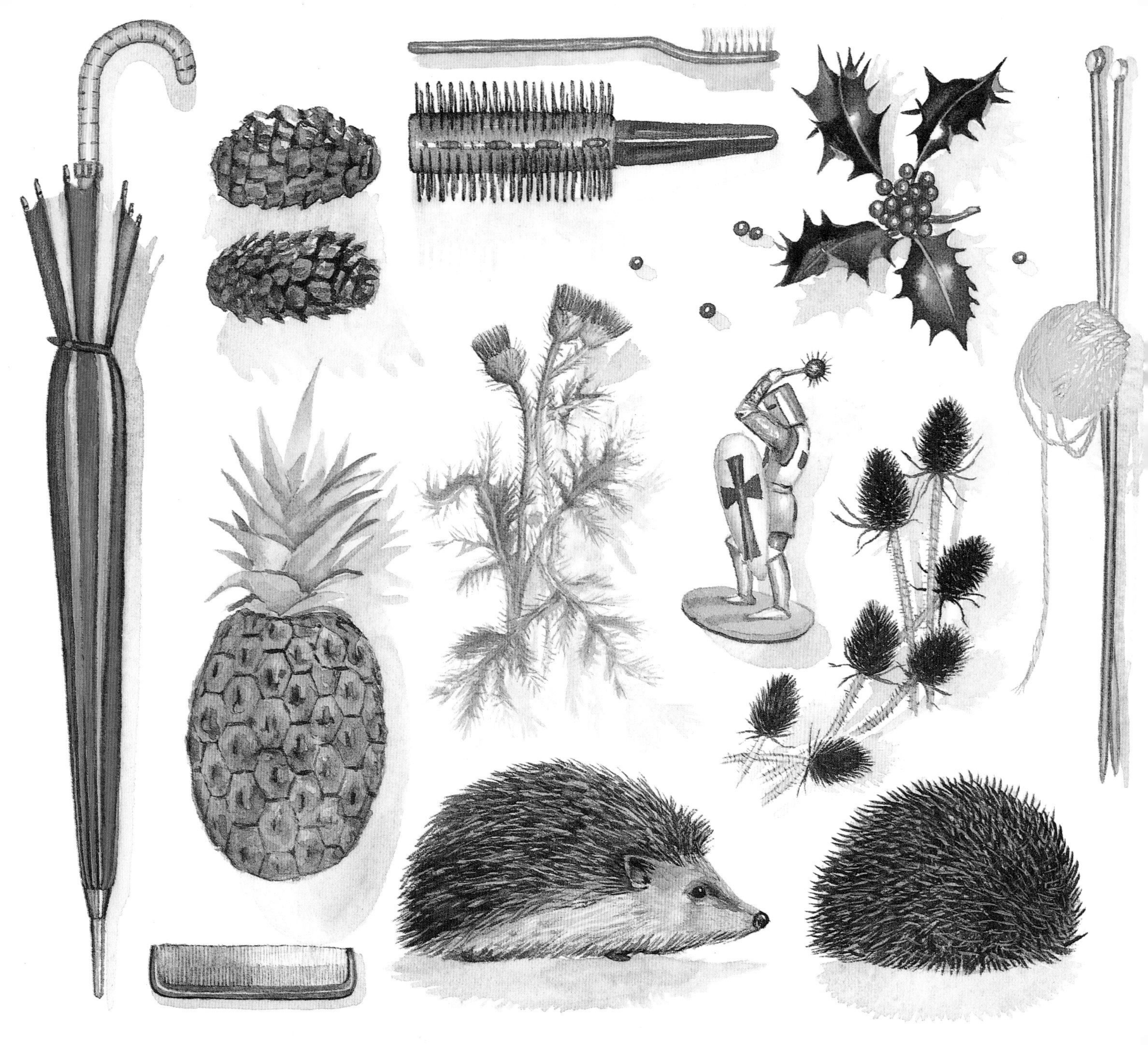

WET THINGS

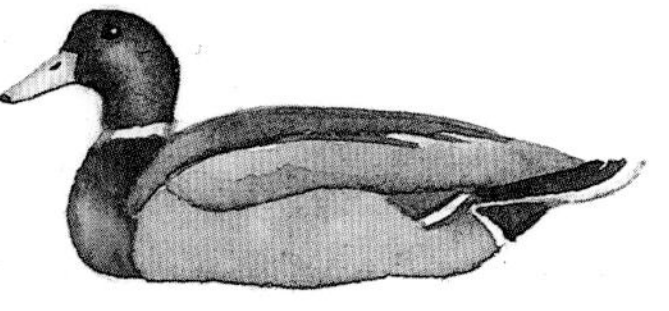

Rain to fill potholes
for puddles and ponds.
Rainbow filled skies ...
through clouds and beyond !
A fish in a bowl
or clothes on the line ,
raincoats and rainhats ,
wellies that shine!

*

Water that gurgles ,
splish , splash and a gluck ,
and water that runs . . .
OFF THE BACK OF A DUCK !

COUNTRY THINGS

A cow and a sheep,
a pig or a horse,
a farmhouse, a barn –
and a tractor of course!
A hedge or a fence,
a stile and a gate,
the harvest, a maypole
and grand village fête!

*

A badger, a rabbit,
a stoat or a weasel?
And there in the sun ...
A FARM CAT CALLED TEAZLE!

EXTRA
FETE
WILD ANIMALS
BY EDEN LAURIE

CITY THINGS

Buses and bikes,
a swing in the park,
bakers, greengrocers —
bright lights in the dark!
Brick walls and railings,
on roads that are wide,
grand railway stations —
a ticket to ride!

*

Rows of town houses
and offices too,
and over a tall wall ...
GIRAFFES AT THE ZOO!

GROCER
BAKERY
BY BUS
RAILWAYS &
TRAINS
A
LO
TIMETABLE
TO THE PARK
ZOO

SMELLY THINGS

An onion, some pepper,
a row of sweet peas,
a lily, some lilacs —
a plate of blue cheese!
A bottle of perfume,
a smelly old sock,
a fish, and a bad egg —
that came as a shock!

*

And now for smell
to delight all our noses,
so sweetly scented ...
A BUNCH OF RED ROSES!

Lilac Soap
Lily
Lily Soap

HOT THINGS

A candle , a curry,
a match that's alight,
a sparkler or rocket —
a light bulb so bright !
An iron , a kettle ,
a mug of hot tea ,
the sun on a nice day,
or a spicy chilli !

*

These things you see
send the temperature higher,
pull your chair closer . . .
AND SIT BY THE FIRE !

SOL-LAR
SUN
CREAM
ENGLAND'S
GLORY

COLD THINGS

Ice-cream and lollies ~
too chilly to hold!
Icicles, ice cubes ~
so slippery and cold!
Skates for the ice rink,
Scots pines in a row,
weather in winter,
the frost and the snow.

*

Things from the Arctic,
things that are Polar,
And there in the garden...
A SNOWMAN IN A BOWLER!

SEASIDE THINGS

Sand-castles with flags on,
a bucket and spade,
a deckchair, a wind-break —
an umbrella for shade!
a seagull, a sea-shell,
a tiny sea-horse,
a towel, sunglasses,
for sunshine of course!

*

A pier with lights,
and amusements aglow,
get to the end, and ...
IT'S ON WITH THE SHOW!

SLEEPY THINGS

Time to curl up,
it's the end of the day,
a bed with a pillow,
a sheet and duvet.
With Neddy the Teddy,
you'll be dreaming soon–
falling asleep with . . .
THE STARS AND THE MOON !